Contents

*S = silver; G = gold; P = platinum; ( ) = the line must be played but cannot be assessed for a Medal;
non-bold type = descant/soprano recorder; bold type = treble/alto recorder.

Sweet Camel

Sarah Watts

Tangalypso

Brian Bonsor

AB 3136

Mouse Tale

Robert Tucker

AB 3136

The Cowboy Sat on the Cactus

Sally Adams

AB 3136

Canzonet

('When lo by break of morning')

Morley arr. Sally Adams

AB 3136

Salsa

David Gordon

AB 3136

Goblins

Paul Harris

AB 3136

Juggling

Pam Wedgwood

Slower and a little sad

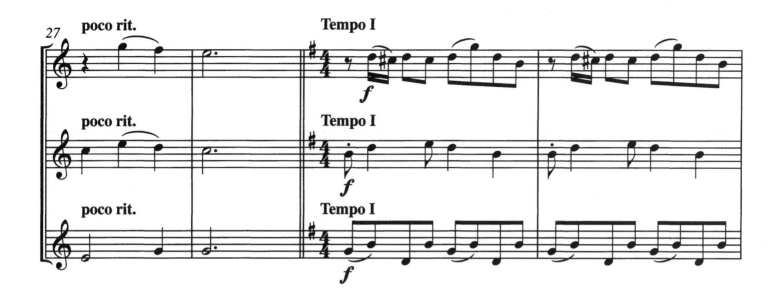

Blues for Max

Sarah Watts

AB 3136

Aria

from *Hail, bright Cecilia*

Purcell arr. Peter Bowman

AB 3136

Pastime with good company

Henry VIII arr. Alyson Lewin

AB 3136

Time to Beguine

John Pitts

AB 3136

Tumblers

Andrew Challinger

Blue Skies and Golden Sands

Brian Bonsor

AB 3136

Three Breezes

Michael Rose

AB 3136

Jenny Pluck Pears

from *The English Dancing Master*, 1651

Trad. English arr. Alyson Lewin

AB 3136

Pure Cheek!

Robert Tucker

AB 3136

El grillo

(Chanson 'The Cricket')

Josquin des Prez arr. Alyson Lewin